Going to America

by Lee S. Justice
illustrated by Marni Backer

HOUGHTON MIFFLIN

BOSTON

"Tell me about the United States of America, Mama," Samuel said.

"America is the golden land," said Mama.

Samuel's father was in America. He had been there for three years.

Samuel's father worked in America. He wanted his family to come to America too. He was saving money so that he could bring his family there.

One day, Mama got a letter from Papa. The letter had some tickets. The family was going to America!

Mama cried. Grandmother cried. Samuel cried. Even Samuel's older brother, Myer, cried.

They were all happy. But they were sad too. Grandmother was not coming with them.

They put their things in a wagon. They
would ride on the wagon to get to the train.
Samuel looked at his house from the wagon.
He watched the house get smaller and smaller.

It was Samuel's first time on a train.
The ride was noisy and bumpy, but Samuel
enjoyed it.

He looked out the window at the fields
and houses.

When they got to the port, a doctor checked each person. "Only healthy people go to America," Myer said.

Then Samuel saw the ship that would take them to America. It was so big!

The trip was long. Each day, Samuel played on the deck with the other children. He also listened to people talking. They spoke many different languages.

Samuel was lucky. He did not get seasick on the ship like Myer. "Ooooh," Myer moaned. Mama held his head.

They slept with many other people on the lower level of the ship.

"Soon we will be in America," Mama said many times.

On the tenth day of their journey,
Samuel heard people shout. He ran to the
deck. "The Statue of Liberty!" someone
shouted. Some people cried. Some cheered.
One man put Samuel on his shoulders so
that he could see.

"Oh, Mama," Samuel shouted. "Look!"
"We are in America!" Mama said.

Everyone got off the ship and went to a big building. There were so many people! Samuel and Myer stayed close to Mama.

They waited in line. Some people were sick. Men put chalk marks on the coats of the sick people. They had to get well before they could leave the building.

"Look strong and healthy!" Mama said. Samuel and Myer tried to look strong and healthy. They didn't get any chalk marks.

13

14

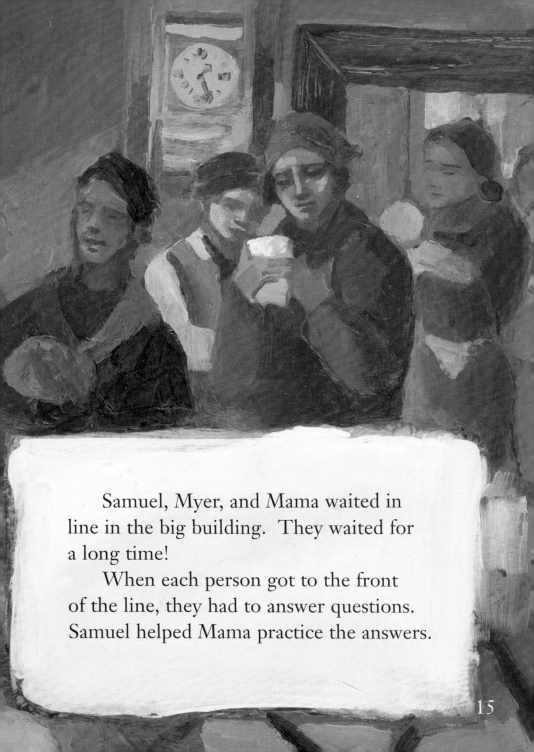

Samuel, Myer, and Mama waited in line in the big building. They waited for a long time!

When each person got to the front of the line, they had to answer questions. Samuel helped Mama practice the answers.

15

Finally, it was Mama's turn. She answered all of the questions. Then a man said everything was all right.

"We are in America now," Mama said. And then she smiled. It was good to see her smile.

Samuel and Myer smiled too.
"Look, it's Papa!" cried Mama.
"Papa!" shouted Myer.

Samuel ran to Papa and got a big hug.
Papa looked a little different. But his hug
was just as Samuel had remembered.

U.S. Red Meat Consumption, by Type*

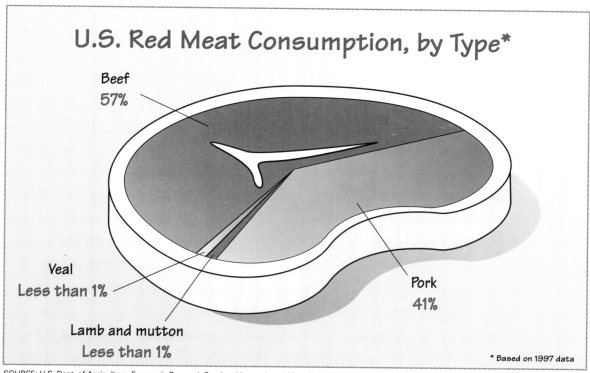

Beef
57%

Veal
Less than 1%

Lamb and mutton
Less than 1%

Pork
41%

* Based on 1997 data

SOURCE: U.S. Dept. of Agriculture, Economic Research Service, *Livestock and Meat Statistics, 1997*

World's Top 5 Soft-Drink Consuming Countries

Annual consumption per capita, in quarts

111.0	86.0	79.3	78.4	78.1
Switzerland	Barbados	Bahamas	United States	Australia

SOURCE: Beverage Marketing Corporation

Food

Top 5 U.S. Soft Drinks*

The U.S. consumes an average total of 13 billion gallons of soft drinks each year.

Billions of cases sold each year

- 1.97B — Coca-Cola Classic
- 1.39B — Pepsi
- 819M — Diet Coke
- 605M — Mountain Dew
- 598M — Sprite

Wholesale sales, based on 1997 data

SOURCE: Beverage Marketing Corporation.

World's Top 5 Coca-Cola Consuming Countries

Servings consumed per person in 1999

- 412 — Mexico
- 395 — USA
- 330 — Chile
- 285 — Australia
- 277 — Norway

SOURCE: Beverage Marketing Corporation

Food

Top 5 U.S. Candy and Snack Products, by Type
(Percentage of total industry sales)

Type	Percentage
Chocolate bars	45.5%
Potato chips and pretzels	22.0%
Cookies	9.4%
Non-chocolate bars	8.7%
Gums	3.4%

Percentage of total industry sales: 0% 10% 20% 30% 40% 50%

SOURCE: *Manufacturing Confectioner*

America's Favorite Snack Sensations
(Percentage of total industry sales)

Other 22.0%

Potato chips 31.9%

Popcorn 8.1%

Snack nuts 8.4%

Pretzels 8.6%

Tortilla chips 21.4%

SOURCE: Snack Food Association

Food

Top 5 Best-Selling U.S. Gum Brands
(By income from annual sales in grocery stores)

Brand	Sales
Wrigley's Extra	$108M
Trident	$76M
Carefree	$74M
Wrigley's Doublemint	$39M
Freedent	$36M

0   $20M $40M $60M $80M $100M $120M

Sales in millions of dollars

SOURCE: Information Resources, Inc.

Putting Food on the Table

About 26% of kids ages 16–17 prepare a full meal for their families one night per week, vs. 8% of 12- to 13-year-olds. How kids ages 12–17 help with family meals:

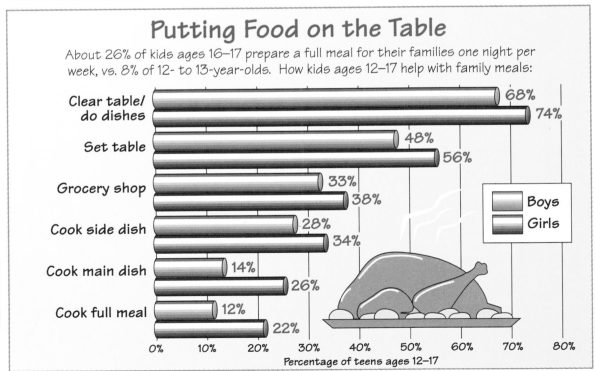

Task	Boys	Girls
Clear table/do dishes	68%	74%
Set table	48%	56%
Grocery shop	33%	38%
Cook side dish	28%	34%
Cook main dish	14%	26%
Cook full meal	12%	22%

0%   10%   20%   30%   40%   50%   60%   70%   80%

Percentage of teens ages 12–17

SOURCE: Based on data from Bruskin-Goldring for the National Pork Producers Council

Food

Top 5 Ice Cream-Consuming Countries in the World

The average American eats about 47 pints of ice cream each year.

Pints per capita, annual consumption

- United States — 47.0
- New Zealand — 37.7
- Denmark — 36.0
- Australia — 32.7
- Belgium/Luxembourg — 31.5

SOURCE: International Ice Cream Association

Ben & Jerry's Top 10 Ice Cream/ Frozen Yogurt Flavors

(By annual sales)

1. Chocolate Chip Cookie Dough
2. Cherry Garcia
3. Chocolate Fudge Brownie
4. New York Super Fudge Chunk
5. Cherry Garcia Frozen Yogurt
6. Chunky Monkey
7. Chocolate Fudge Brownie Frozen Yogurt
8. English Toffee Crunch
9. Peanut Butter Cup
10. Chubby Hubby

SOURCE: Ben & Jerry's Homemade

Food

Who Sells the Most Fast Food?

In 1998, sales of hamburgers at fast-food restaurants totalled $43 billion. (Percentage of total industry sales)

Taco Bell
$4.8B

Pizza Hut
$4.7B

KFC
$4.0B

Wendy's
$4.6B

McDonald's
$17.1 B

Burger King
$7.8B

Food

SOURCE: Technomic, McDonald's, Burger King

Fast-Food Frenzy

McDonald's serves an average of 38 million people every day at 23,500 restaurants in 109 countries. Average daily customer visits (in millions):

United States — 19.7M

Europe — 7.6M

Asia/Pacific — 7.5M

Latin America — 1.8M

Canada — 1.5M

5M 10M 15M 20M

Daily customer visits

SOURCE: Based on data from McDonald's International

America's Fast-Food Feasters

Nearly one-quarter of all fast-food in the U.S. is bought by kids 17 and under. (Percentage of total sales by age)

17 and younger
23%

Over 35
45%

18–34
32%

SOURCE: Based on data from *USA Today*

Food

What Tops Pizza?

(Most requested toppings,
by percentage of all pizzas sold)

Pepperoni
43%

Onions
4%

Others
7%

Vegetables
13%

Mushrooms
14%

Sausage
19%

Food

Top 10 Products in the Grocery Store

(Average annual grocery sales in dollars)

FROZEN ICE CREAM ORAN FROZEN CON

- $1.8B — Coke Classic
- $1.7B — Pepsi
- $1.2B — Campbell's soup
- $936M — Kraft cheese
- $927M — Folgers coffee
- $846M — Diet Coke
- $810M — Snackwell's
- $759M — Marlboro Lights
- $750M — Budweiser beer
- $681M — Tropicana Pure Premium orange juice

Sales in millions/billions of dollars

$1.5B
$1B
$500M
0

SOURCE: Based on data from *USA Today*

Food

Candy Companies with the Sweetest Sales
(By percentage of total annual U.S. candy sales)

Tootsie Roll 1.8%

Ferrero 1.6%

Other 13.1%

Hershey 25.1%

Sathers 2.8%

Sunmark 5.2%

Nestle 6.1%

Life Savers 7.0%

M&Ms/ Mars 18.5%

Adams 8.0%

Wrigley 10.8%

Food

SOURCE: American Wholesale Marketers Association

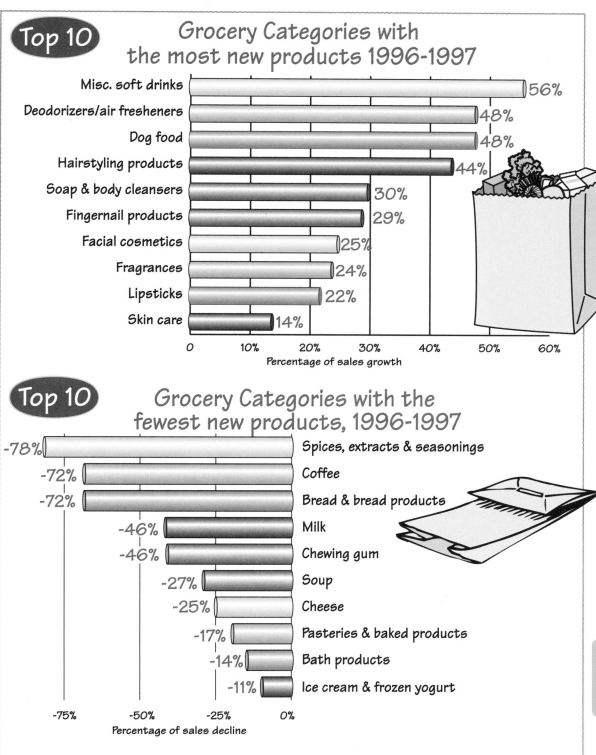

Top 10 Grocery Categories with the most new products 1996-1997

Category	Percentage of sales growth
Misc. soft drinks	56%
Deodorizers/air fresheners	48%
Dog food	48%
Hairstyling products	44%
Soap & body cleansers	30%
Fingernail products	29%
Facial cosmetics	25%
Fragrances	24%
Lipsticks	22%
Skin care	14%

Percentage of sales growth

Top 10 Grocery Categories with the fewest new products, 1996-1997

Percentage of sales decline	Category
-78%	Spices, extracts & seasonings
-72%	Coffee
-72%	Bread & bread products
-46%	Milk
-46%	Chewing gum
-27%	Soup
-25%	Cheese
-17%	Pasteries & baked products
-14%	Bath products
-11%	Ice cream & frozen yogurt

Percentage of sales decline

Food

SOURCE: Based on data from *Marketing Intelligence Service, Ltd.*

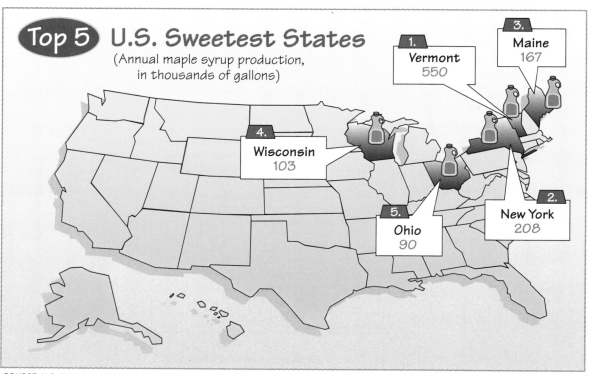

Top 5 U.S. Sweetest States
(Annual maple syrup production, in thousands of gallons)

1. Vermont 550
2. New York 208
3. Maine 167
4. Wisconsin 103
5. Ohio 90

SOURCE: U.S. Agricultural Statistics Service

Sales Get Spicy

Spices are among the hottest-selling items at the grocery store. The top 10 dry seasonings by growth in sales volume from 1989 to 1997:

Growth in sales volume

- Cumin 153%
- Cinnamon stick 65%
- Garlic 58%
- Garlic powder 45%
- Bay leaves 45%
- Ginger 39%
- Onion powder 37%
- Cloves 32%
- Poultry seasoning 30%
- Cream of tartar 29%

SOURCE: Based on data from *USA Today*

Food

The Food Pyramid

The U.S. Department of Agriculture (USDA) has created this recommended balance of food groups for good nutrition.

Fats, Oils, & Sweets
USE SPARINGLY

Meat, Poultry, Fish, Dry Beans, Eggs, & Nuts Group
2–3 SERVINGS DAILY

Milk, Yogurt, & Cheese Group
2–3 SERVINGS DAILY

Vegetable Group
3–5 SERVINGS DAILY

Fruit Group
2–4 SERVINGS DAILY

Bread, Cereal, Rice, & Pasta Group
6–11 SERVINGS DAILY

Food

SOURCE: U.S. Department of Agriculture

Computers

It's hard to believe that digital computers have only been around since 1946. And, considering where we are with laptops and PDAs, it's hard to imagine that the first computer was a huge monster that weighed 30 tons!

It didn't have transistors, integrated circuits, disk drives, not even a keyboard or a monitor. Those things hadn't been invented yet! It couldn't do word processing or play games or send e-mail. In fact, a $40 calculator today has more total computer power than that first computer!

Today, computers are everywhere. In only a short period of time, they have become as much a part of everday American life as televisions, microwaves, and telephone answering machines. PCs sit on desktops and are carried in briefcases and backpacks. Tiny computers are installed in cars, stoves, and hundreds of other products. People of every age, and in every kind of job, use computers. In general, young people are more comfortable with using computers than are older people. Today's kids have grown up with computers. In fact, many young people are finding that their computer skills can be a great source of extra money. Lots of

Kidbits Tidbits
- The first computer, named ENIAC, weighed 30 tons and filled a room. Today's laptop computers are 1,000 times faster than ENIAC.
- The most popular thing to do on the Internet is read and send e-mail.
- By late 1999, some 92 million Americans had gone online; 71 million had used the Web.
- The largest online service provider in 1997 was America Online, or AOL, with some 8 million subscribers.
- Males use the Internet most, but the gap is closing. In 1999, males made up about 54% of users, and females accounted for about 46%.

teens make money writing computer programs, maintaining computer bulletin boards, repairing computers, even teaching old folks how to zip around the World Wide Web!

One of the most popular uses of computers is to go "online." Surfing the Net, you can visit people and places all over the world, including sports teams, museums, parks, and schools. You can search encyclopedias, dictionaries, newspapers, and other reference sources, (a great way to do research for school and business reports!). You can "chat" with friends, movie stars, musicians, and politicians.

The best way to explore the Internet is via the World Wide Web. The Web is a collection of standards that make it easier to navigate the Internet and access information. The Web displays information in interconnected "pages" that are linked to one another by key words or phrases that are highlighted. Point to a highlighted word, click the mouse, and you instantly jump to another page. Each page has an address. For example, the Web address for the White House is: *http://www.whitehouse.gov*

Going online also lets you send e-mail from your computer to someone else's computer. You can shop for everything from candy to Cadillacs. You can make plane reservations and find recipes. You can download games and other programs to your own computer. You can even take a virtual tour of Mars, go inside the eye of a hurricane, or "chat" with some of the world's most famous people!

Kidbits Tidbits
- By 2000, more than 62 million PCs in the U.S. accessed the Internet regularly—a huge jump from about 15 million PCs in 1996.
- By late 1999, there were approximately 800 million pages on the World Wide Web.
- Bill Gates, one of the two guys who started Microsoft, is the richest person in the world. By 1999 he was worth almost $61.7 billion.

Computers

Profile: Teen Use of Technology
(Kids in 7th through 12th grades)

Computer Use vs. Other

Average number of hours a week teens spend:

Watching TV	18
Talking on the phone	7
Using a computer	4

Number of hours

Daily Use

Percentage of teens who use the following at least once a day:

Stereo	85%
Calculator	67%
Telephone answering machine	46%
Computer	44%
Video/computer games	40%
VCR	39%

Percentage of teens

Computer Use

Percentage of teens who have used a computer to:

Play computer games	93%
Write school report	89%
Use Internet for school report	56%
Chat on Internet/send e-mail	48%

Percentage of teens

SOURCE: Based on data from Gallup Organization

Do I Really Need a Computer?

Percentage of teens who say they could easily live without:

Item	Percentage
Video/computer games	82%
VCR	49%
Phone answering machine	38%
Stereo	31%
Calculator	29%
TV	28%
Computer	23%

0%   20%   40%   60%   80%

Percentage of teens

SOURCE: Based on data from Gallup Organization

Computers

Teen Use of the Internet and Online Services

(By location of use)

Net: Used any service
- 54%
- 40%
- 27%

Internet/World Wide Web
- 38%
- 29%
- 16%

America Online
- 37%
- 22%
- 18%

Prodigy
- 17%
- 10%
- 8%

CompuServe/WOW!
- 13%
- 9%
- 5%

Microsoft Network
- 5%
- 3%
- 3%

Used Anywhere
Used at School
Used at Home

0%   10%   20%   30%   40%   50%

Percentage of teens

Computers

SOURCE: Based on data from Teenage Research Unlimited, Inc.

Profile: Teen Online Preferences, by Gender
(Percentage of users in gender group)

Males	Females

Who Checks Out Internet Sites More?

56%

42%

Who Chats More Online?

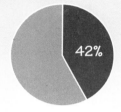

50%

48%

Who Does More Research Online?

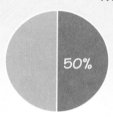  

40%

47%

Who E-mails More Online?

 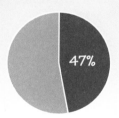

40%

42%

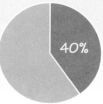 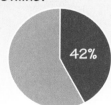 

SOURCE: Based on data from Teenage Research Unlimited, Inc.

Computers

Profile: Teen Online Preferences, by Gender
(Percentage of users in gender group)

Males	Females

Who Says Entertainment Sites Are Best?

52%   48%

Who Says Sports Sites Are Best?

47%   23%

Who Says Music Sites Are Best?

48%   58%

Who Says Game Sites Are Best?

44%   31%

SOURCE: Based on data from Teenage Research Unlimited, Inc.

Computers

Online At Home

Most common activities of people with home computers and online access:

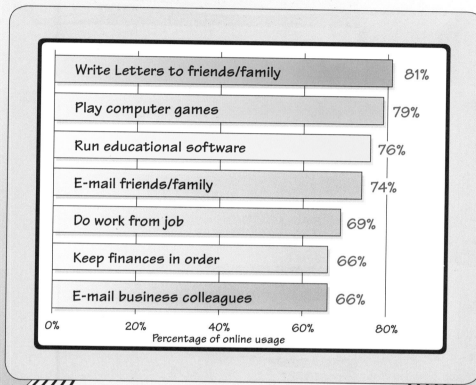

Activity	Percentage
Write Letters to friends/family	81%
Play computer games	79%
Run educational software	76%
E-mail friends/family	74%
Do work from job	69%
Keep finances in order	66%
E-mail business colleagues	66%

Percentage of online usage

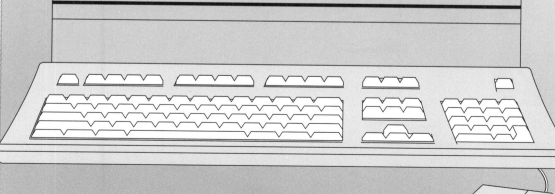

SOURCE: Based on data from Roper Starch for Lexmark

Kiddin' Online

Most kids ages 9–13 know about the Internet and more than half of them have gone online. The most popular activities of kids online:

Activity	Percentage
Chat with others	45%
Play games	40%
Information for fun	38%
Information for school	28%
E-mail	20%
Other	10%
Don't know	1%

Percentage of Internet usage

Computers

SOURCE: Based on data from *Sports Illustrated for Kids* Omnibus

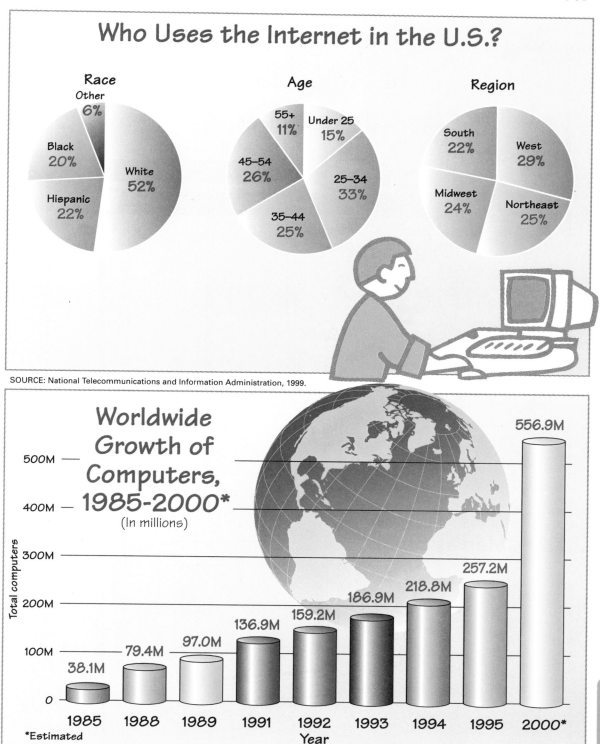

Who Uses the Internet in the U.S.?

Race

Other
6%

Black
20%

Hispanic
22%

White
52%

Age

55+
11%

Under 25
15%

45–54
26%

25–34
33%

35–44
25%

Region

South
22%

West
29%

Midwest
24%

Northeast
25%

SOURCE: National Telecommunications and Information Administration, 1999.

Worldwide Growth of Computers, 1985-2000*
(In millions)

Total computers

500M

400M

300M

200M

100M

0

38.1M — 1985
79.4M — 1988
97.0M — 1989
136.9M — 1991
159.2M — 1992
186.9M — 1993
218.8M — 1994
257.2M — 1995
556.9M — 2000*

Year

*Estimated

SOURCE: Based on data from Karen Petska-Juliussen and Egil Juliussen, *8th Annual Computer Industry Almanac*

Computers

Top 10 PC Companies in the U.S. Market

Since 1992, the rankings of the top-selling companies in the U.S.
PC market have changed. IBM and Dell now hold top positions.

U.S. Shipments
(In millions)

Dell	9.3M
IBM	8.7M
Compaq	5.0M
Packard Bell NEC	2.7M
Gateway 2000	2.2M
Hewlett-Packard	2.0M
Toshiba	1.4M
Apple	1.2M
Acer	1.1M
Micron	.6M

0   2M   4M   6M   8M   10M

Number of units

U.S. Market Share

Compaq 16.0%

Others 29.2%

Micron 2.2%

Acer 3.5%

Toshiba 4.6%

Packard Bell NEC 8.8%

Hewlett-Packard 6.6%

IBM 8.7%

Gateway 2000 7.1%

Apple 4.1%

Dell 9.3%

Computers

SOURCE: Based on data from International Data Corp.

Top 10 PC Companies in the Worldwide Market

Worldwide Shipments
(In millions)

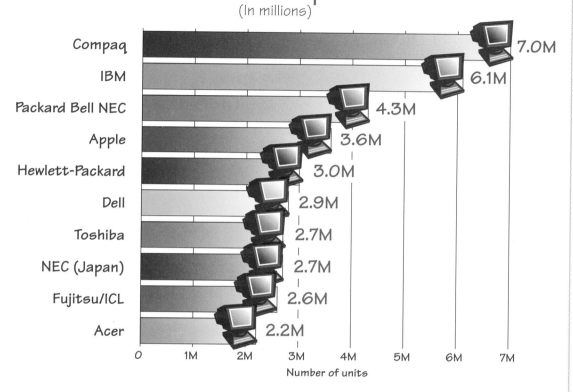

Company	Shipments
Compaq	7.0M
IBM	6.1M
Packard Bell NEC	4.3M
Apple	3.6M
Hewlett-Packard	3.0M
Dell	2.9M
Toshiba	2.7M
NEC (Japan)	2.7M
Fujitsu/ICL	2.6M
Acer	2.2M

0   1M   2M   3M   4M   5M   6M   7M
Number of units

Worldwide Market Share

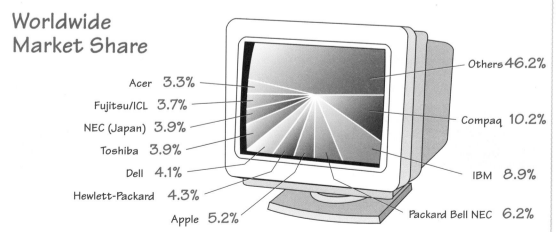

Acer 3.3%
Fujitsu/ICL 3.7%
NEC (Japan) 3.9%
Toshiba 3.9%
Dell 4.1%
Hewlett-Packard 4.3%
Apple 5.2%
Others 46.2%
Compaq 10.2%
IBM 8.9%
Packard Bell NEC 6.2%

Computers

SOURCE: Based on data from International Data Corp.

Top 10 Best-Selling Computer Games

1	Sim City 3000	Electronic Arts
2	Baldur's Gate	Interplay
3	Cabela's Big Game Hunter 2	Activision
4	Starcraft Expansion: Brood Wars	Havas Interactive
5	Half-Life	Havas Interactive
6	Monopoly Game	Hasbro Interactive
7	Deer Hunter II 3-D	GT Interactive
8	Frogger	Hasbro
9	Deer Avenger	Havas Interactive
10	Sid Meier's Alpha Centauri	Electronic Arts

SOURCE: Based on data from PC Data, Reston, VA

Top 10 Best-Selling Educational Software

1	Blue's ABC Time Activities	Humongous
2	Rugrats Movie Activity Challenge	Mattel Media
3	Jumpstart First Grade	Havas Interactive
4	Kid Pix Studio Delux	Mattel Media
5	Jumpstart Preschool	Havas Interactive
6	Learn to Speak Spanish	Mattel Media
7	Jumpstart Second Grade	Havas Interactive
8	Rugrats Adventure Game	Mattel Media
9	Blue's Birthday Adventure	Humongous
10	Jumpstart Kindergarten II	Havas Interactive

SOURCE: Based on data from PC Data, Reston, VA

Computers

Top 10 Most Visited Web Sites

In December 1996, only 627,000 domain names had been registered. By September 1999, some 10 million domain names were registered.

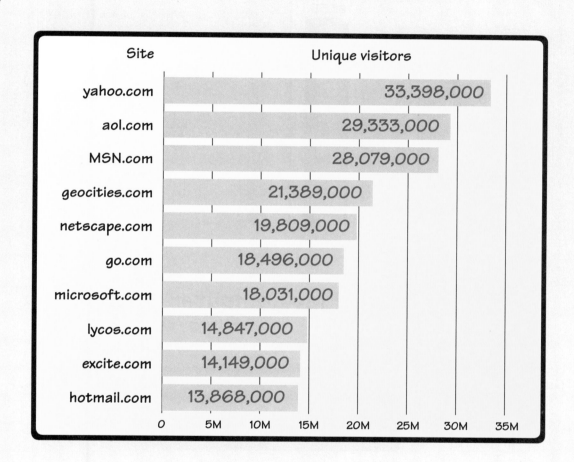

Site	Unique visitors
yahoo.com	33,398,000
aol.com	29,333,000
MSN.com	28,079,000
geocities.com	21,389,000
netscape.com	19,809,000
go.com	18,496,000
microsoft.com	18,031,000
lycos.com	14,847,000
excite.com	14,149,000
hotmail.com	13,868,000

0   5M   10M   15M   20M   25M   30M   35M

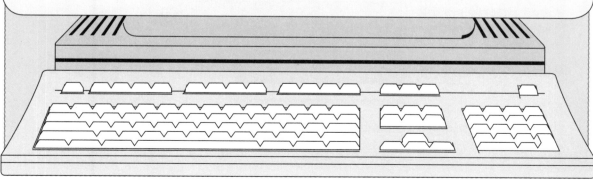

Computers

SOURCE: *Media Matrix*, Aug, 1999

Paying to Play

Entertainment software sales have almost doubled in the last five years.

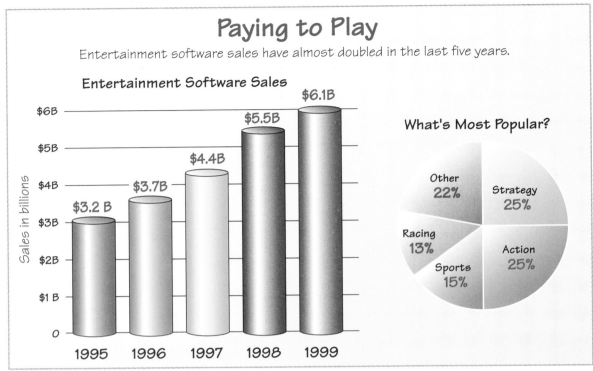

Entertainment Software Sales

What's Most Popular?

- Other 22%
- Strategy 25%
- Racing 13%
- Action 25%
- Sports 15%

SOURCE: Interactive Digital Software Association

Why Do People Play Computer Games?

In 1999, the gaming industry's sales were up more than 100% since 1996.

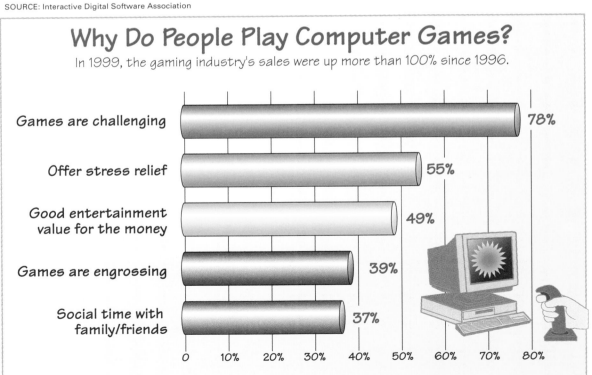

- Games are challenging — 78%
- Offer stress relief — 55%
- Good entertainment value for the money — 49%
- Games are engrossing — 39%
- Social time with family/friends — 37%

SOURCE: Interactive Digital Software Association

The Growth of Personal Computer Shipments and Revenues, 1983 to 1998

Shipments
(In millions of units)

Number of units

100M

80M — U.S. shipments

Worldwide shipments

60M

98.4M

47.9M

40M

34.6M

21.3M

20M 18.6M

11.1M

6.2M 9.3M

0

1983   1989   1994   1998

Year

Revenues
(In millions of U.S. dollars)

Millions of U.S. dollars

$200M

$217.4M

$150M — U.S. revenue

Worldwide revenue

$94.5M

$100M

$81.9M

$50M $40.4M

$37.3M

$11.0M

$19.7M

$6.5M

$0

1983   1989   1994   1998

Year

SOURCE: Based on data from Dataquest

Computers

Top 10 Countries with the Most Computers Per Person, Estimated for 2000

Country	Number of computers per 1,000 people
United States	580.0
Australia	525.7
Norway	515.4
Canada	511.9
Denmark	510.2
Sweden	508.9
Finland	505.0
New Zealand	499.2
The Netherlands	450.3
Switzerland	443.7

Number of computers per 1,000 people

Computers

SOURCE: Based on data from Karen Petska-Juliussen and Egil Juliussen, *8th Annual Computer Industry Almanac*

Index

A

Abdul, Paula, 152
Abortion, 271
Accidental deaths, 20–21, 115–116
  types of, 118–119
Acquired immunodeficiency syndrome (AIDS). See AIDS
Actors and actresses, 172, 178–179, 181, 198–199, 202–203
Adams, 294
Adams, John Quincy, 237
Adidas, 65
Advertising
  athletes in, 235
  commercial preferences, 170–171
  for food, 283
  for movies, 186
  online, 311
  in sports sector, 205
  on television, 157
Aerobics, 49–50
Aerosmith, 151–152
African Americans
  computer use by, 86–87
  high school dropouts, 84
  population by region, 13
  substance abuse by, 113–114
  television preferences of, 157
AIDS
  children with, 122
  in cities, 122
  cumulative cases of, 123
  people living with, 121
Air pollution, 259–260
Alabama, 144
Aladdin, 184, 194
Alaska
  population, 14
  wetlands in, 262
Alcohol, 108
  absorption of, 109
  annual consumption, 110
Alda, Alan, 172
Alice in Wonderland, 177
All About Eve, 200
"All My Children," 164
Allen, Paul, 40
Alley, Kirstie, 178
"Ally McBeal," 180
Amadeus, 190
American Beauty, 200–201

American Pie, 193
Amusements, 126, 131
Analyze This, 193
Anderson, Gillian, 179
Andorra, 22–23
"Angry Beavers," 167
Animals. See also Pets
  endangered, 268
  fastest, 269
  threatened, 267–268
Anka, Paul, 137
Anschutz, Phillip, 40
Apple, Fiona, 153
Aguilera, Christina, 149
Arkansas
  income in, 43
  pets in, 243
As Good As It Gets, 200
Asian Americans, population by region, 13
Asner, Ed, 172
"As the World Turns," 164
Athletes. See Pro sports; Sports
Atlanta, GA, 122
Attitudes, 270–281
  influences on, 278
Austin Powers, 193
Australia
  computers in, 314–315
  death rates in, 117
  ice cream consumption in, 289
  life expectancy in, 22–23
  threatened animals in, 267
Austria, 80
Automobiles
  accidents, 103, 118–119
  racing, 205, 227

B

Babe, 195, 200
Backstreet Boys, 146, 149, 152
Bacrot, Etienne, 68
Baker, Kathy, 179
Bakersfield, CA, 260
Ballmer, Steven, 40
Bangladesh, 27–28
Baranski, Christine, 181
Baseball, 48–50, 52, 79
  base stealers in, 221
  highest career batting averages in, 219
  home run hitters, 218
  most career games in, 219
  oldest stadiums, 223
  RBI leaders in, 220
  run-scorers, 222
  salaries in, 234

top earners in, 223
top teams, 224
Basinger, Kim, 203
Basketball, 46–50, 52, 56, 79. See also National Basketball Association
  injuries from, 54
Bassett, Angela, 199
Bates, Kathy, 198, 202
Batman, 192, 197
Batman Forever, 192
Batman Returns, 187
Beanie Babies, 69
Beatles, 137, 142
Beauty and the Beast, 184–185, 194, 200
Beck, 151
Belgium, 80, 289
Ben-Hur, 182–183, 190
Ben & Jerry's, 192
Benigni, Roberto, 202
Bennett, Tony, 154
Bergen, Candice, 172, 178
"Between Brothers," 157
Beverages, consumption of, 284
"Beverly Hills, 90210," 169
Bicycle riding, 46–51, 54, 133
Big Daddy, 193
Bill Haley and the Comets, 137
Billiards, 49–50, 56
Binoche, Juliette, 203
Birds, 241, 246, 250, 257
  households with, 247, 254–255
  population of, 238
  threatened, 267–268
  and vet costs, 251–253
Blair Witch Project, The, 196
Blanchett, Cate, 198
Blethyn, Brenda, 198
Blink-182, 146
Boating, 51, 130
"Bold and the Beautiful, The," 164
Bolton, Michael, 155
Bon Jovi, 146
Books
  countries buying, 80
  favorite types of, 279
  types of, 74, 81
Boston, 143
Bowfinger, 193
Bowling, 46–50, 56, 130
Boxing, 51
Boy Scouts of America, 124, 129

Braugher, Andre, 179
Braveheart, 201
Braxton, Toni, 155
Brazil
  carbon dioxide production, 263
  population of, 26–28
  threatened animals in, 267
  VCRs in, 191
Bringing Out the Dead, 196
Brooks, Garth, 143–144
B-52s, 152
"Buena Vista I," 162
Buffalo, NY, 167
Buffett, Warren, 40
Bulgaria, 115
Burnett, Carol, 172
Bush, George and Barbara, 237

C

Cabaret, 190
Cable TV, 156–157
  growth of, 160
  households with, 163
  top networks, 161, 169
  top services, 160
Cage, Nicolas, 198, 202
Caine, Michael, 199, 203
California
  hazardous waste sites, 266
  population, 14
Cameron, James, 201
Camping, 46–50, 126
Canada
  carbon dioxide production, 263
  computers in, 314–315
  death rates in, 117
  life expectancy in, 23
  math scores in, 95
  threatened animals in, 267
Cancer, 20–21, 116
Candy, 31, 283, 287, 294
Carbon dioxide emissions, 259–260
Carbon monoxide
  pollution by, 261
  production of, 263
Carey, Mariah, 142, 155
Carney, Art, 172
"Carol Burnett Show, The," 173
Carrey, Jim, 198–199
Catholicism, 18, 24, 84
Cats, 241, 257
  breeds, 244
  households with, 245, 247–248, 254–255

I N D E X

lifespan of, 257
population of, 238
top states for, 245
and vet costs, 251–253
CD-ROMs, 75, 88
CDs (compact discs), 140
Census Bureau, 8–9
Chapman, Tracy, 155
"Cheers," 173, 180
Cheese, 282–284, 297
Chess, 68
Chicago, IL, 122
Children
  activities of, 128
  with AIDS, 122
  causes of death among, 20
  cost of raising, 39
    and fast food, 291
  dreams of wealth, 33
  favorite athletes, 233
  and food preparation, 288
  households with and
    without, 16
  influences on, 278
  and Internet, 99, 277, 306
  languages spoken by, 15
  music purchases by, 141
  population by region, 12
  projected population to
    2050, 26
  and religion, 25
  sports most popular with,
    48
  television preferences,
    166–167
  television viewing time, 161
China
  carbon dioxide production,
    263
  computers in, 315
  as origin of U.S. population,
    11
  population of, 26–28
  religion in, 25
  saving habits in, 39
  threatened animals in, 267
Chinese language, 15
Christie, Agatha, 69
Cigarettes
  acquisition of, 114
  consumption of, 103, 112
  grade level and, 115
  teenagers and, 113
Cities, U.S., 9, 122, 260
Civil Action, A, 195
Clapton, Eric, 151, 153–155
Cline, Patsy, 144
Clothes, 58–67
  cool, 63–65

mall space allotted to, 61
spending on, 66
  for sports, 45
  teen care, 60
  top companies, 67
Coburn, James, 203
Coca-Cola, 283, 286, 293
Cole, Natalie, 153–154
College(s), 83
  costs of, 83, 91
  and football draft, 216
  freshmen, profile of, 90
  largest, 92
  selection of, 96
Collins, Phil, 153
Colombia, 267
Colorado, pets in, 243
Colvin, Shawn, 153–154
Comedy movies, 199–200
Comedy shows, 178, 180–181
Commercials
  favorite, 171
  least favorite, 170
  top advertisers, 168
Computers, 298–315
  countries with most, 315
  countries with most per
    person, 314
  first, 298–299
  games, 312
  growth of, 307, 313
  at home, 305
  for homework, 87
  importance of, 301
  versus other activities, 300
  purchase of, 70
  in school, 86, 99
  top companies, 308–309
  top games, 310
Concerts, 138–139
Connecticut, income in, 43
Costa Rica, 22
Costello, Elvis, 151
Costner, Kevin, 201
Counting Crows, 153
Country albums, 144
"Cousin Skeeter," 167
Cows, 241
Creed, 146
Crosby, Bing, 137
Crow, Sheryl, 153, 155
Crowe, Russell, 202
Cruise, Tom, 198–199
Curtis, Jamie Lee, 199
Cutthroat Island, 187
Cyberpets, 69
Cyrus, Billy Ray, 144
Czech Republic, 115

D
"Dallas," 158
Daly, Tyne, 172
Dances with Wolves, 185,
  201
Dancing, 135
Danson, Ted, 178
Dave Matthews Band, 147
Death(s). See also
    Accidental deaths
  causes of, 20–21, 103, 116
Death rates, 19
  highest, 117
Delany, Dana, 179
Del Toro, Benicio, 203
Delaware, population, 14
Demme, Jonathan, 201
Dench, Judi, 198, 203
Denmark, 29, 263, 289, 314
Depardieu, Gerard, 199
Diabetes, 21, 116
Diamond, Neil, 137
Dion, Celine, 153, 154, 155
Disney, 167
District of Columbia, 122
  income in, 43
  population, 14
Divorce rates, 18
Dogs, 257
  birthdays, 246
  breeds, 242
  costs of, 256
  households with, 243,
    247–248, 254–255
  lifespan of, 257
  population of, 238
  of Presidents, 237, 241
  top states for, 243
  and vet costs, 251–253
Dominican Republic, 11
Drama movies, 198
Drama shows, 179–180
Driving Miss Daisy, 200
Dylan, Bob, 154

E
Eagles, 135, 139, 142–143
Earth Day, 259
Eastern Orthodoxy, 24
Eastwood, Clint, 201
Ecuador, 267
Electronics, types owned, 76
Elementary school,
    enrollment, 82–83, 85
Ellison, Lawrence, 40
El Salvador, 11
Eminem, 146, 153
Emmy awards, 172–173,

178–181
Empire Strikes Back, The,
  188–189, 197
Enemy of the State, 195
English Patient, The, 201
Entertainment, 68–81
"Entertainment Tonight," 162
Environment, 258–269
"E.R.," 157, 159, 169, 180
Ethiopia, 28
E.T.: The Extraterrestrial,
  184, 188–189, 197
Evita, 200
Exercise, 77, 126
  age and, 104
  with equipment, 46–47
  reasons for, 105

F
Falco, Edie, 179
Falk, Peter, 172, 179
Families, size of, 17
Fast food, 290, 291
Fayanju, Seyi, 83
Finland, 115, 263, 314
Fish, 240, 250, 268
Fishing, 47–50, 56, 72, 133
Fleetwood Mac, 143
Florida
  population, 14
  wetlands in, 262
Fonda, Peter, 198
Food, 282–297
  consumption of, 284
  declining products, 295
  growth products, 295
  preparation of, 77, 288
  in school, 100–101
  top products, 293
Food pyramid, 297
Foo Fighters, 152
Football, 48–50, 52, 79
    See also Super Bowl
  best passers, 213
  most touchdowns in, 211
  salaries in, 234
  top draft suppliers, 216
  top earners, 217
  top–paying positions in, 217
  top rushers, 212
  top scorers, 212
Forces of Nature, 195
Foreign-born population, 8,
  11
  countries of birth for, 11
Forrest Gump, 184, 185,
  188, 194, 197, 200–201
Foster, Jodie, 198, 202
Fox, Michael J., 178

France
carbon dioxide production, 263
computers in, 315
deaths in, 115, 117
life expectancy in, 23
math scores in, 95
religion in, 25
saving habits in, 39
Franz, Dennis, 179
"Frasier," 159, 180
Freeman, Morgan, 199
"Fresh Prince of Bel Air," 169
"Friends," 159, 162, 169
From Here to Eternity, 190, 200
Frozen yogurt, 289

G

Games, 75, 80, 310
Gandhi, 190
Gardening, 72, 126
Gates, William III, 40, 299
"General Hospital," 164
Georgia, population, 14
Gerbils, 240, 250
Germany
book-buying in, 80
computers in, 315
death rates in, 117
dreams of wealth in, 33
heights in, 29
religion in, 25
saving habits in, 39
VCRs in, 191
Ghost, 185
Gibson, Mel, 201
Gigi, 190
Girl Scouts of U.S.A., 124, 129
Gladiator, 201
Glow bowling, 44
Goldberg, Whoopi, 203
Golden Globes, 174, 198–200
Gold, Julie, 154
Golf, 46–47, 50, 55, 72
Gone With the Wind, 158, 189–190, 200
Gooding, Cuba, Jr., 203
Gordon, Irving, 154
Grammer, Kelsey, 178
Grammy awards, 153–155, 174
Grand Slam champions, 231
Grant, Hugh, 199
Greece, 22
Green Card, 200
Greenhouse gases, 258, 261

Guinea pigs, 240, 250, 257
Gymnastics, 51

H

Haas family, 40
Hackman, Gene, 203
Hamburgers, 100, 283, 290
Hamsters, 240, 250, 257
Handball, 51
Hanks, Tom, 198, 202
Hanson, 134
Harden, Marcia Gay, 203
Harper, Valerie, 172
Harroun, Ray, 205
Haunting, The, 196
Hayes, Sean, 181
Hazardous waste, 266
Health, 102–123
Heart disease, 20–21, 116
Heaton, Patricia, 178
Henley, Don, 151
Hershey, 294
High-definition television, 156–157
High school
dropouts, 84
enrollment, 82–83, 85
Hiking, 47, 49, 51, 126
Hill, Lauryn, 151, 152, 154
"Hill Street Blues," 173
Hingis, Martina, 45, 228
Hispanic Americans
computer use by, 86–87
high school dropouts, 84
population by region, 13
and poverty, 9
substance abuse by, 113–114
HIV infection, 20–21.
See also AIDS
cumulative cases of, 123
Hockey, 50–52, 79
salaries in, 234
top earners, 226
top scorers, 225
Holbrook, Hal, 172
Home Alone, 185, 188
"Home Improvement," 169
Homework, setting for, 96
Homicide and legal
intervention, deaths from, 20–21
Hong Kong, 11, 22–23
Hootie and the Blowfish, 153
Hopkins, Anthony, 202
Horror, 183, 193, 196
Horseback riding, 50
Horse racing, 226

Horses, 241, 257
households with, 247, 254–255
lifespan of, 257
population of, 238
and vet costs, 251–253
House on Haunted Hill, 196
Houston, TX, 122, 260
Houston, Whitney, 137, 153–154
Hungary, 115
Hunter, Holly, 198, 202
Hunt, Helen, 178, 199, 202
Hunting, 51

I

Ice cream, 289
Iceland, 22–23
Ice skating, 50
Idaho, pets in, 243, 245
Illinois, population, 14
Imbruglia, Natalie, 153
Inchon, 187
Independence Day, 188, 192, 194, 197
India, 11, 26–28, 263, 267
Indianapolis 500, 205, 227
Indonesia, 26–28, 267
In–line skating, 49–50
Internet, 299
advertising on, 311
children and, 277, 306
music sales on, 148
versus other activities, 280
teenagers and, 302–304
use of, 306–307
Iowa, pets in, 245
Irons, Jeremy, 198, 202
Isaak, Chris, 151
Islam, 24
Israel, 22, 95
Italy, 94, 117, 315

J

Jackson, Janet, 152
Jackson, Michael, 135–136, 142–143
Jamiroquai, 151
Japan
carbon dioxide production, 263
computers in, 315
death rates in, 117
life expectancy in, 22–23
population of, 27
religion in, 25
saving habits in, 39
studying abroad in, 94

VCRs in, 191
Jaws, 197
Jell-O, 283
Jennings, Will, 154
"Jeopardy," 162
Jesus Jones, 153
Jeter, Michael, 181
Jet skiing, 51
Jewel, 152
Jobs
earnings, 32
hours per week, 32
worries about, 32, 275
John, Elton, 135, 137, 155
Johnson, Kristen, 181
Jolie, Angelina, 203
Jones, James Earl, 179
Jones, Quincy, 154
Jones, Tommy Lee, 203
Jordan, Michael, 206, 233, 235
Judaism, 18, 24
Jurassic Park, 182, 184, 188, 192, 194, 197

K

Kentucky Derby, 226
Kentucky Fried Chicken, 290
Kid Rock, 146, 149
Kidman, Nicole, 199
King, Carole, 142
Kirkpatrick, Wayne, 154
KISS, 136
Kluge, John, 40
Knotts, Don, 172
Korea, 11, 95, 115, 315
Korman, Harvey, 172
Kravitz, Lenny, 151
Kudrow, Lisa, 181
Kwan, Michelle, 44–45

L

"L.A. Law," 180
Lahti, Christine, 179
Landau, Martin, 203
Lange, Jessica, 198, 202
Lang, Jonny, 134
lang, k.d., 152, 155
Larroquette, John, 172
Last Action Hero, The, 187
Last Emperor, The, 190
"Law & Order," 180
Leachman, Cloris, 172
Learned, Michael, 172
Led Zeppelin, 143
Lennox, Annie, 152, 155
Levi Strauss, 59
Libraries, 71

I N D E X

Life, 195
Life Savers, 294
Lima, OH, 167
Limp Bizkit, 146, 149
Lion King, The, 183–184, 188, 194, 197, 200
Lithgow, John, 178
Little Mermaid, The, 184–185
Living Color, 152–153
Lizards, 250
Lloyd, Christopher, 179
Los Angeles, CA, 122, 260
Lost World, The, 192
Louis-Dreyfus, Julia, 181
Louisiana, wetlands in, 262
Luxembourg, 289
Luyendyk, Arie, 227

M

M&M/Mars, 294
Madagascar, 267
Madonna, 151, 152, 199
Magazines, 69, 73
  children's, 78
Maine
  maple syrup production in, 296
  pets in, 245
Malls, 77
  and clothing sales, 59
  shopping in, 42
  space allotment in, 61
Mammals, threatened, 267–268
Marriage
  popular times of year, 9
  rates, 18
Martial arts, 51
Martin, Ricky, 149
Martinique, 23
Mary Poppins, 200
"Mary Tyler Moore Show, The," 173
"M*A*S*H," 158, 173
Massachusetts, income in, 43
Mathematics, country rankings in, 95
Matrix, The, 195
McDonald's, 168, 170–171, 283, 290–291
McDormand, Frances, 202
McEntire, Reba, 147
McFerrin, Bobby, 153–155
McLachlan, Sarah, 155
McTeer, Janet, 199
Meat Loaf, 142
Mendes, Sam, 201
Menken, Alan, 154

Metallica, 146
Metcalf, Laurie, 181
Mexico
  accidental deaths in, 115
  carbon dioxide production, 263
  as origin of U.S. population, 11
  studying abroad in, 94
  threatened animals in, 267
Miami, FL, 122
Michael, George, 154
Michigan
  hazardous waste sites, 266
  population, 14
Midler, Bette, 153–154, 199
Midwest, population, 12–13
Miller, Justin, 157
Minghella, Anthony, 201
Minnesota, wetlands in, 262
Mississippi
  income in, 43
  pets in, 243
Mrs. Doubtfire, 200
Money, 30–43
Monkees, 137
Montana
  income in, 43
  pets in, 243, 245
  population, 14
Moore, Earl, 40
Moore, Mary Tyler, 172
Morissette, Alanis, 152–154
Movies, 126, 128, 130, 132, 182–203, 280
  awards. *See* Golden Globes; Oscars
  comedy and musical, 199–200
  drama, 198
  highest-grossing, 188–189
  most expensive, 187
  quickest-grossing, 192
  ratings, 183, 192
  revenues, 185
  on television, 177
MTV Video Music Awards, 151–153
Mullally, Megan, 181
Mummy, The, 196
"Murphy Brown," 180
Music, 128, 132, 134–155
  acquisition of, 135, 149
  best-selling, 137, 142–143, 149
  "cool," 146
  Grammy awards, 153–155
  Internet sales of, 148
  MTV awards, 151–153

performers, 146
  road shows, 136
  sales, 134, 140–141, 148, 150
Musicals, 199–200
My Fair Lady, 190

N

'N Sync, 146, 147, 149
National Basketball Association, 205
  coaches, 207
  draft pick positions, 209
  players with most games, 207
  salaries in, 234
  top earners, 209
  top players, 208
  top scorers, 206
  top teams, 210
National Football Association, 205, 212–214, 216–217
National Merit Scholars, 89
Native Americans, population by region, 13
Nelson, Craig T., 178
Nestlé, 294
Netherlands, 29, 263, 314
Neuwirth, Bebe, 181
Nevada, pets in, 243, 245
Newark, NJ, 122
New Kids on the Block, 139
New Hampshire
  pets in, 245
  population, 14
Newhouse family, 40
New Jersey
  educational spending, 82
  hazardous waste sites, 266
  population, 14
New Mexico
  income in, 43
  pets in, 243
Newspapers, 69, 73
New York
  hazardous waste sites, 266
  income in, 43
  maple syrup production in, 296
  population, 14
New York City, NY, 122
New Zealand, 289, 314
Nicholson, Jack, 199, 202
Nielsen ratings, 157
Nigeria, 27–28
Nike, 59, 64–65, 67, 171
Nirvana, 153
No Doubt, 152

Nolte, Nick, 198
North Dakota
  pets in, 245
  population, 14
Northeast, population, 12–13
"Northern Exposure," 180
Norway, 29, 80, 314
Notting Hill, 193
"NYPD Blue," 180

O

O'Connor, Carroll, 172
O'Connor, Sinead, 151–152
Ohio
  maple syrup production in, 296
  population, 14
Oil spills, 266
Oklahoma, pets in, 243
Oleynik, Larisa, 157
Olivier, Laurence, 172
101 Dalmations, 184, 189
One-parent households, 16
Online services
  advertising in, 311
  preferences in, 303–304
  shopping, 64
  use of, 299, 302
On the Waterfront, 190
"Oprah Winfrey Show," 162
Orbison, Roy, 155
Oregon, pets in, 245
Oscars, 174, 201–203
  top nominees, 200
  top winners, 190

P

Pacino, Al, 198, 202
Pagers, 81
Pakistan, 27–28
Palance, Jack, 203
Paltrow, Gwyneth, 199, 202
Papua New Guinea, 267
Paquin, Anna, 203
Patch Adams, 195
Patinkin, Mandy, 179
Pearl Jam, 151–152
Penn, Michael, 153
Pennsylvania
  hazardous waste sites, 266
  population, 14
Pepsi, 64, 171, 286, 293
Perlman, Rhea, 172, 181
Personal computers, 313.
  See also Computers
Peru, 267
Pesci, Joe, 203
Pets, 236–257, 271. *See also*

Animals
combinations of, 247–248
households with, 241
and house type, 254
income and, 255
lifespans of, 257
ownership of, 239
population of, 238
of Presidents, 237, 241
responsibility for, 237, 249
specialty/exotic, 240
spending on, 237,
251–253, 256
veterinarian care for, 250
Pfeiffer, Michelle, 198
Philadelphia, PA, 122
Philippines, 11, 267
"Picket Fences," 180
Pierce, David Hyde, 181
Pink Floyd, 139, 142–143
Pinocchio, 184
Pizza, 100, 282–283, 292
Pizza Hut, 290
Player, The, 200
Pocahontas, 194
Poland, 11, 115
Population, 8–29
by age and sex, 10
children, in 2050, 26
foreign-born, 8, 11
projected, 27–28
by race, 13
by region, 12–13
Portugal, 115
Poverty, 9
"Practice, The," 180
Presley, Elvis, 135, 137
Pretty Woman, 185
Pro sports, 204–235
and endorsement deals, 235
most popular athletes in, 233
salaries in, 234
Protestantism, 18, 24

R
Rabbits, 240–241, 250, 257
Racquetball, 51
Radio, 77, 132, 144–145
Rage: Carrie 2, The, 196
Raitt, Bonnie, 154–155
Recommended daily dietary
allowances, 106
Recreation, 124–133
sales of, 131
Recycling, 259, 264–265
Religion(s)
among believers, 18
children and, 25
top five, 24

R.E.M., 151–152
Reptiles, 237, 240, 250, 268
Return of the Jedi, 188, 197
Reynolds, Burt, 178
Rhode Island, population, 14
Rice, Tim, 154
Richards, Michael, 181
Richardson, Miranda, 199
Rimes, LeAnn, 134
Rivers, 262
Riverside-San Bernardino,
CA, 260
Robbins, Tim, 199
Roberts, Julia, 199, 202
Rodents, 240, 250
Rollerskating, 50
Rolling Stones, 135,
137–139, 147
Roots, 158
"Roseanne," 178
Ruehl, Mercedes, 203
"Rugrats," 167
Runaway Bride, 193
Rush, Geoffrey, 198, 202
Russia, 27–28, 95, 117
Ruth, Babe, 205, 218

S
Santana, 149
San Francisco, CA, 122
Sarandon, Susan, 202
SAT scores, 89, 94
Saving Private Ryan, 195
Schindler's List, 201
School, 82–101
abroad, 94
and income, 83, 85
spending on, 97
teenagers and, 272–273
Sci-fi, 193, 197
Seal, 153–155
Sealfon, Rebecca, 83
"Secret Life of Alex Mack,
The," 157
"Seinfeld," 157, 162, 169,
180
Sex
and activity preferences, 125
and athletic shoe purchases,
62
and computer use, 86–87,
299, 303–304
death rates by, 19
and income, 34
and life expectancy, 19,
22–23
and magazine preferences, 78
and movie preferences, 183
and music sales, 150

and National Merit
Scholarships, 89
and pet responsibility, 249
population by, 10
and radio station prefer-
ences, 145
ratio in population, 9
and reading preferences, 279
and school sports
opportunity, 205
and spending, 41
and sports injury, 53
and sports participation,
46, 50–51
and substance abuse, 108,
113
and television viewing
habits, 175
Shakespeare in Love,
200–201
Shoes
new, 61
for sports, 53, 62
Shore, Dinah, 172
Silence of the Lambs, The,
201
Simon and Garfunkel, 142
"Simpsons, The," 169
Sims, Tommy, 154
Sixth Sense, The, 196
Skateboarding, 50
Skating, 49–50, 54
Skerritt, Tom, 179
Skiing, 50–51, 54, 57
Sleepy Hollow, 196
Slovenia, 95
Smashing Pumpkins, 136, 151
Smith, Will, 151
Snack products, 287
Snakes, 250
Snowboarding, 51, 57
Snow sports, 45, 57
*Snow White and the Seven
Dwarfs,* 184, 189, 194
Soap operas, 164
Soccer, 46, 48, 50, 52, 54,
56, 79
Soderbergh, Steven, 201
Softball, 48–50, 130
Soft drinks
consumption of, 284–285
top countries for, 285
Sony, 64–65
Sorvino, Mira, 203
Sound of Music, The, 189
South Africa, 263
South Dakota, population, 14
South, population, 12–13
Spacey, Kevin, 202, 203

Spain, 22–23, 94–95, 117
Spears, Britney, 146, 149
Spielberg, Steven, 201
Sports, 44–57, 77, 126,
132, 280
clothing, 45
injuries from, 53–54
interest in, age and, 55
most popular, 46–48
participation in, 49
professional, 204–235
rules of, understanding, 52
on television, 157, 164, 167
Springsteen, Bruce, 143,
147, 154
Star Wars, 182, 188–189
Star Wars Trilogy, 194
States, U.S.
cat-loving, 245
dog-loving, 243
income per person in, 43
least populated, 14
most populated, 14
spending on education, 82
Steubenville, OH, 167
Stigmata, 196
Stine, R. L., 69
Stir of Echoes, 196
Stone, Sharon, 198
Stone Temple Pilots, 153
Strait, George, 147
Streisand, Barbra, 137, 139
Substance abuse, 102
common drugs, 110
by high school seniors, 111
Suicide, 20–21, 116
Sunmark, 294
Super Bowl
most attended, 215
teams with most
appearances, 214
Superfund hazardous waste
sites, 263
Surfing, 51
Swank, Hilary, 198, 202
Sweden, 22, 29, 314
Swimming, 46–50
Switzerland
accidental deaths in, 115
book buying in, 80
computers in, 314
life expectancy in, 23
math scores in, 95

T
Taco Bell, 290
Taiwan, 11, 95
Tandy, Jessica, 199
Technology

INDEX

in schools, 88
teenagers and, 300
Teenagers
accidental death and, 119
advertising preferences,
170–171
and computer purchase, 70
concerns of, 32, 274–275
favorite activities, 132
favorite musical performers,
146
favorite radio station
formats, 145
income sources, 38
and Internet, 302–304
as mall shoppers, 42
participation in sports,
49–51
population by region, 12
and school, 272–273
spending habits, 33, 36
spending habits of, 41
spending power of, 35
sports most popular with,
48
and substance abuse, 108,
111
and teachers, 98
and technology, 300
television preferences, 166
television viewing time, 161
weekly income, 33
work hours per week, 32
Television, 72, 77, 128, 132,
156–181, 280, 300–301
Emmy awards, 172–173,
178–181
high-definition, 156–157
highest ratings, 158
movies on, 177
ownership of, 76, 176
popularity of, 165
specials, 174
teenager preferences in, 166
top shows, 159, 166–167
top syndicated programs,
162
viewing preferences in, 175
viewing time, 161, 174
Ten Commandments, The,

189
Tennis, 46, 50, 130
top earners, 228
top Grand Slam champions,
231
top prize money earners in,
232
top U.S. Open champions,
230
top Wimbledon champions,
229
*Terminator 2: Judgment
Day,* 185, 187
Texas
pets in, 243
population, 14
wetlands in, 262
*There's Something About
Mary,* 195
Thomas, Jay, 181
Thompson, Emma, 198, 202
Titanic, 135, 182–183,
187–190, 200–201
TLC, 149, 151–152
Tobacco use, 113
Tomei, Marisa, 203
Tomlin, Lily, 172
Tom Petty and the
Heartbreakers, 151
Tommy Hilfiger, 65
Tootsie Roll, 294
Top Gun, 183, 185
Torn, Rip, 181
Total Recall, 187
"Touched by an Angel," 159
Toxic waste, producers of,
267
Toy Story, 194
Toys, top selling, 70
Track and field, 46, 50
Trading cards, 31, 79
Travolta, John, 199
True Lies, 187
Turtles, 240, 250
Tuscaloosa, AL, 167
Twain, Shania, 147, 149
Two-parent households, 16

U

U2, 136, 138, 139, 152

Ullman, Tracey, 172
Unforgiven, 201
United Kingdom
carbon dioxide production,
263
computers in, 315
death rates in, 117
as origin of U.S. population,
11
religion in, 25
saving habits in, 39
studying abroad in, 94
VCRs in, 191
U.S. Open, 230
Utah, educational spending,
82

V

Vacations, 124, 128
activities on, 129
Van Dyke, Dick, 172
Van Halen, 151
Varsity Blues, 195
VCRs, 76, 183
countries with most, 191
Vermont
maple syrup production in,
296
pets in, 245
population, 14
Veterinarians, 237, 250
costs of, 251–253
Video(s), 182–203
best–selling, 184, 194
horror, 183, 193, 196
MTV awards for, 151–153
sci–fi, 193, 197
Video games, 68, 75, 128,
300
Video rentals, 132, 184, 193
categories of, 193
top, 185, 195–197
Vietnam, 11, 267
Volleyball, 48–50

W

Walton family, 40
War and Peace, 187
Ward, Sela, 179
Washington, D.C.. *See*

District of Columbia
Washington, Denzel, 198
Washington (state), pets in,
245
Waste
hazardous, 266
production of, 259, 263
toxic, producers of, 267
types of, 264
Water skiing, 51
Waterworld, 187
West, population, 12–13
West Side Story, 190
West Virginia
income in, 43
pets in, 243, 245
"West Wing, The," 180
Wettig, Patricia, 179
Wheeling, WV, 167
"Wheel of Fortune," 162
White House, web page, 299
*Who's Afraid of Virginia
Woolf?,* 200
"Wild Thornberries," 167
Wild, Wild West, 193
Wiest, Dianne, 203
"Will and Grace," 180
Williams, Robin, 199, 203
Wimbledon, 229
Winters, Jonathon, 181
Wisconsin, maple syrup
production in, 296
Woods, Tiger, 45, 205
World Wide Web, 299
most visited, 311
use of, 307
Wrestling, 51
Wrigley, 294
Wyoming
pets in, 243, 245
population, 14

Y

"Young and the Restless,
The," 164
Young, Neil, 151
Youngstown, OH, 167

Z

Zemeckis, Robert, 201